Summer of My German Soldier

'Many people will hear this story about a Jewish girl and a German prisoner. It shows that people can be friends . . .'

During the last years of the Second World War, a group of German prisoners are sent to work in the small town of Jenkinsville, USA. When Patty Bergen, a young Jewish girl, meets one of them in her father's shop, she knows he is the friend she is looking for. But Germans and Americans are enemies . . .

Patty does not have many friends. Her parents are not kind to her and the only person she can talk to is Ruth, a woman who works for the Bergen family. Bored and unhappy through the long, hot summer months, Patty thinks about her new friend, Anton. When he escapes from prison, she decides to help him – and puts herself in danger . . .

Bette Greene was born in 1934 and grew up in a small town in Arkansas like the one in this book. Like Patty, she is Jewish, and she often felt different from other people. She remembers the Second World War and the soldiers who were sent to prisons near her home: 'In one prison there was a young German who did not want to fight, kill or die. He wanted to be free, and a young Jewish girl helped him.'

Bette Greene went to university in France and the USA and wrote many short stories. *Summer of My German Soldier* was published in 1974. She has written five more books for young people.

She now lives in Massachusetts, USA, with her husband, who is a doctor, and their two children.

OTHER TITLES IN THE SERIES

The following titles are available at Levels 2, 3 and 4:

Level 2
The Birds
Chocky
The Canterville Ghost and the Model Millionaire
The Diary
Don't Look Behind You
Don't Look Now
Emily
The Fox
Flour Babies
The Ghost of Genny Castle
Grandad's Eleven
The Lady in the Lake
Money to Burn
Persuasion
The Railway Children
The Room in the Tower and Other Ghost Stories
Simply Suspense
Treasure Island
Under the Greenwood Tree
The Wave
We Are All Guilty
The Weirdo

Level 3
Black Beauty
The Black Cat and Other Stories
The Book of Heroic Failures
Calling All Monsters
A Catskill Eagle
Channel Runner
The Darling Buds of May
Dubliners
Earthdark
Forrest Gump
The Fugitive
Jane Eyre
King Solomon's Mines
Madame Doubtfire
The Man with Two Shadows and Other Ghost Stories
More Heroic Failures
Mrs Dalloway
My Family and Other Animals
Not a Penny More, Not a Penny Less
Rain Man
The Reluctant Queen
Santorini
Sherlock Holmes and the Mystery of Boscombe Pool
StarGate
The Thirty-nine Steps
Thunder Point
Time Bird
The Turn of the Screw
Twice Shy

Level 4
The Boys from Brazil
The Breathing Method
The Burden of Proof
The Client
The Danger
Detective Work
The Doll's House and Other Stories
Dracula
Far from the Madding Crowd
Farewell, My Lovely
Glitz
Gone with the Wind, Part 1
Gone with the Wind, Part 2
The House of Stairs
The Locked Room and Other Horror Stories
The Mill on the Floss
The Mosquito Coast
The Picture of Dorian Gray
Strangers on a Train
White Fang

For a complete list of the titles available in the Penguin Readers series please write to the following address for a catalogue: Penguin ELT Marketing Department, Penguin Books Ltd, 27 Wrights Lane, London W8 5TZ.

Summer of My German Soldier

BETTE GREENE

Level 3

Retold by Karen Holmes
Series Editor: Derek Strange

PENGUIN BOOKS

PENGUIN BOOKS

Published by the Penguin Group
Penguin Books Ltd, 27 Wrights Lane, London W8 5TZ, England
Penguin Books USA Inc., 375 Hudson Street, New York, New York 10014, USA
Penguin Books Australia Ltd, Ringwood, Victoria, Australia
Penguin Books Canada Ltd, 10 Alcorn Avenue, Toronto, Ontario, Canada M4V 3B2
Penguin Books (NZ) Ltd, 182–190 Wairau Road, Auckland 10, New Zealand

Penguin Books Ltd, Registered Offices: Harmondsworth, Middlesex, England

First published in Great Britain by Hamish Hamilton Children's Books Ltd 1974
This adaptation published by Penguin Books 1996
1 3 5 7 9 10 8 6 4 2

Illustrations by Rowan Clifford

Printed in England by Clays Ltd, St Ives plc
Set in 11/13 pt Monophoto Bembo by
Datix International Limited, Bungay, Suffolk

To the teacher:

In addition to all the language forms of Levels One and Two, which are used again at this level of the series, the main verb forms and tenses used at Level Three are:

- past continuous verbs, present perfect simple verbs, conditional clauses (using the 'first' or 'open future' conditional), question tags and further common phrasal verbs
- modal verbs: *have* (*got*) *to* and *don't have to* (to express obligation), *need to* and *needn't* (to express necessity), *could* and *was able to* (to describe past ability), *could* and *would* (in offers and polite requests for help), and *shall* (for future plans, offers and suggestions).

Also used are:

- relative pronouns: *who*, *that* and *which* (in defining clauses)
- conjunctions: *if* and *since* (for time or reason), *so that* (for purpose or result) and *while*
- indirect speech (questions)
- participle clauses.

Specific attention is paid to vocabulary development in the Vocabulary Work exercises at the end of the book. These exercises are aimed at training students to enlarge their vocabulary systematically through intelligent reading and effective use of dictionary.

To the student:

Dictionary Words:

- When you read this book, you will find that some words are darker black than the others on the page. Look them up in your dictionary, if you do not already know them, or try to guess the meaning of the words first, without a dictionary.

Before you read:

1 This story happens in the USA during the Second World War. What do you know about this war? Which countries were fighting? Why they were fighting?

2 Patty Bergen and her family are Jewish. What do you know about the Jews? What happened to many Jewish people in Europe during the Second World War?

3 Look at the pictures in the book. How do you know that the story is set almost fifty years ago? How are people's clothes, hair, cars, etc. different from yours?

4 *Summer of My German Soldier* is about a small town called Jenkinsville in Arkansas, USA. Find Arkansas on a map of the USA. Think about films you have seen and other books you have read about America. What do you think this town was like to live in?

CHAPTER ONE

Everybody in our town – Jenkinsville, Arkansas, the USA – was waiting for the train to arrive at the railway station. I saw Chester, the black man who worked at my father's shop.

'Hi, Chester,' I said. 'Isn't this exciting? I've never seen a German before.'

'No, neither have I,' he replied.

'The train's coming!' Jimmy Wells shouted.

Suddenly everyone was silent. A few minutes later, the train stopped at the platform.

'Where are they?' a woman asked.

Jimmy Wells pointed. 'There.'

Two guards carrying guns climbed from the train. The German soldiers followed. They wore ordinary blue shirts and trousers but they had the word 'prisoner' in black letters on their backs.

'Nazis!'* the woman shouted.

One prisoner smiled and waved. Maybe he did not understand that these people were angry. The prisoners and the guards climbed into a lorry and drove away.

I walked home. Ruth, the black woman who worked in our house, was in the garden.

'I saw the German prisoners,' I said. She did not reply. Her son was a soldier in Europe, fighting Hitler* and the Nazis, and she worried about him.

I found my young sister Sharon, and Ruth served lunch. Later, I decided to walk to my father's shop and tell him about the prisoners.

* Between 1939 and 1945, there was a great war in Europe – the Second World War. The German **leaders** were the National Socialists, or 'Nazis'. The head of Germany was Adolf Hitler. The USA joined the war in December 1941 to fight against the Germans.

I tried to tell my father about the German prisoners but he was not interested.

'Be good,' Ruth said.

'I always try to be good,' I replied. 'My mother and father still get angry with me all the time.'

♦

Jenkinsville was a small town and our shop was the biggest in it. When I arrived, my father was talking to a man.

'Hello,' I said. My father turned and looked at me without a smile.

'Why are you here?' he asked.

'Is this your daughter?' the man said. 'What's your name?'

'Patricia Ann Bergen.'

'That's a pretty name for a pretty girl.' He gave me a sweet. I did not want it, but I said thank you and went over to my mother. She was talking to Mrs Fields.

'That's a pretty dress,' Mrs Fields said.

'Ruth told her to wear it,' my mother said. 'But just look at her hair. It's terrible. You know, Patricia is always so untidy. Sharon is like me. Her dresses and her hair have to be tidy. Sharon's never any trouble.' My mother did not like me. My mother – and Sharon – were both beautiful. I was not. I was thin and my nose was too long.

Later, I tried to tell my father about the German prisoners but he was not interested.

'Be quiet. I'm reading my newspaper,' he said and turned away.

♦

The next Sunday morning, we went to my grandparents' house in Memphis. My father did not want to go; he did not like my grandfather and grandmother.

My mother slept in the car. I looked at her. I loved her very much but nothing I did made her happy. I kissed her. She opened her eyes.

'Stop it,' she said. 'I'm trying to sleep.'

'Sorry,' I said and moved away.

'Why don't you visit us?' my grandmother asked.

My grandfather was standing at the door when we arrived. He kissed me.

'Welcome, my oldest grandchild – you're already a young woman.'

Grandmother came out of the kitchen and kissed my mother, Sharon and me. I went into the kitchen and talked to her while she was cooking.

'Why don't you visit us?' she asked.

'I do!'

'I asked your mother to bring you here on the train. She always says you're too busy.'

'My mother said that? Well, she's telling a lie.'

Grandmother **nodded**. 'OK. Next week you take the train by yourself and we'll spend the day together. I'll buy you a new dress.'

♦

My uncles and aunts arrived and we began to eat.

'We hope that we shall be together for many years,' Grandfather said. 'And that Hitler and his Nazis all die and our dear President Roosevelt stays healthy. *L'chayim*!'

The family talked about the war and the Jews* in Europe.

'Why are we talking about the war?' my mother asked. 'Can't we talk about happy things like parties and clothes?'

'Grandfather's sending us to New York,' Aunt Dorothy said. 'It's business, but I'm going to shop and visit the theatre.'

'Why are you sending them to New York?' my mother asked in a hurt voice. 'And why can't I go too? Why do my brothers get a holiday and not me? You give everything to the boys.'

'Your brothers are different. They always like what we give them. You never want anything when it belongs to you,' Grandfather said.

CHAPTER TWO

I was helping my father at the shop a few days later when a lorry stopped outside and two guards jumped out. 'All right!' they shouted. 'Everybody out.' Ten young men climbed out of the lorry. They came into the shop. I saw the black letters 'prisoner' on their shirts but they looked pleasant. Didn't they know they were losing the war? Didn't they know they were walking into a Jewish shop?

My father spoke to the guards. 'Can I help you?'

'These prisoners are working in the fields. It's too hot – they need hats.' He pointed at one prisoner who had black hair. 'Reiker speaks English. He'll speak for all of them.'

* During the Second World War, Hitler's Nazis killed millions of Jewish people in Europe.

The men looked at the hats. Reiker asked my father for a mirror. He spoke good English. Then he walked across the shop to where I was and looked at the pens and paper.

'Can I help you?' I asked.

He smiled. 'Yes, please. I don't know the English word for this.' His eyes were green.

'It's a pencil **sharpener**,' I said.

'Ah, yes.' He looked at me. I thought he liked me.

'What colour do you want?' I asked.

'You choose,' Reiker said. He was nice. Was he a bad man? He was a Nazi. He laughed and for a second we were friends. I knew he was not a bad man.

'Can I ask you a question?' I asked him. 'Who taught you to speak English so well?'

'My mother was English and my father worked in England. He was a teacher. What's your name?'

'Patricia Ann Bergen. My friends call me Patty.'

'My name is Frederick Anton Reiker. My friends call me Anton. I hope you will call me Anton, Patty.'

'OK,' I said but I was too shy to say his name. 'What did you do before the war?'

'I studied to be a doctor.'

He paid for the pencil sharpener. 'Goodbye, Patty.'

'Goodbye, Anton,' I said. 'I hope you'll be OK.'

He turned to go. I closed my eyes. Oh God, I thought, can Frederick Anton Reiker be my friend? I'll never ask for anything again. And please keep him safe.

'Patty!' Anton's voice. I opened my eyes. He was pointing at something. 'Sell this ring to me. The one with stones like **diamonds**.'

The ring was ugly and cheap. 'Not this one?' I asked, thinking he was making a mistake. He nodded, dropped the money into my hand and walked out of the shop, smiling a different, happier smile.

I wanted to talk to someone about Anton. My mother was

'It's a pencil sharpener,' I said.

serving a customer and she did not want to speak to me. I went over to Sister Parker who worked in our shop.

'That was interesting,' I said. 'The Germans came in to buy things.'

'I don't think Nazis are interesting,' Sister Parker replied. 'I saw you with one of them, talking and laughing. Did you like him?'

She frightened me. Suddenly, I did not want her to know that I liked Anton.

♦

I left the shop and went to Edna Louise Jackson's house. The Jacksons were the richest family in town. Edna liked boys. I could talk to her about Anton.

'Today I met somebody I really liked,' I said.

'A boy?'

'Yes . . . Well, no! He's not a boy, he's a man.'

'How old is he?'

'Maybe twenty, twenty-one.'

'Are you going to see him again?' Edna asked.

'No. He can't go out – he's a German from the prison.'

'A German prisoner? But, Patty, that's as bad as going out with a black man!'

'It isn't!' I shouted.

'It is! God is on the side of America in the war. Germans are bad people.'

Angry, I left her house. 'Well, *he* isn't. He's a very good man,' I said. 'And one day, we're going to meet again. I have to go home now.'

CHAPTER THREE

On Thursday I went to Memphis on the train. Grandma took me to have lunch at an expensive hotel. She told me she was

'A German prisoner? But, Patty, that's as bad as going out with a black man!'

worried. Her two sisters and their families were in Luxembourg and the Nazis were in Luxembourg, too.

'They're probably OK,' I said.

We went shopping and she bought me skirts and shoes.

'I'll see you next Thursday,' I said. 'Don't buy me anything. I just want to be with you.'

'Oh Patricia, my love, I can't see you next Thursday. Grandfather and I are going on holiday.'

She told me she was sorry but I stopped listening. She did not really want to see me.

'Don't worry about it, Grandmother,' I said, and my voice was very cold. 'It's really not important.'

I climbed into the train and sat down. After it left the station, I began to cry.

♦

The summer was hot, dry and endless. The town was very quiet. Nothing happened. All the other girls in the town had gone on holiday. There was nobody for me to talk to. Ruth was busy working and my little sister Sharon played with her friends every day. There was nothing to do. I read all my books and the library was closed so I couldn't get more. I went to the shop and my father sent me home.

Sometimes I went on my bicycle out to the prison. I looked for Anton but I did not see him. The only thing I liked to do was to go to my **hideout**, an empty room over the garage, a forgotten place. It was difficult to get into because the stairs were broken; only I could climb in there.

One day Freddy Dowd came to talk to me. My father did not like me to play with Freddy because his family was very poor.

'Hello,' Freddy said. 'What are you doing?'

'Playing Hit the Wheel. When a car goes past you have to hit the wheels with a stone.'

A car came past, an old slow car. We threw the stones – then, suddenly, crash! The *window*! The family in the car looked at me.

I ran. Oh God, what have I done now? I hid in the field behind our house. I felt sick.

Later I went to find Ruth. She could help me. I told her about the car window. For a long time she said nothing, then she asked, 'Was the family in the car white or black? Did you know them?'

I shook my head. 'I didn't know them. They were white people.'

Ruth nodded and opened her bag. She took out some money.

'You find the man who drives that car and ask him how much a new window costs. Right?'

I loved her. She only had a little money but she wanted to help me. I was just leaving the house when I saw the green car coming down the street. My father! The car stopped and he got out, his face like ice. He came towards me fast.

'I can explain . . . It was an accident!' I said.

But he was not listening. 'Come here!' he shouted.

I walked towards him and he hit me across the face. The world went black, then. He hit me again and again. He **hated** me, I could see that. I hated him. I tried not to cry. He took off his **belt** and hit my legs.

'No! Please!' I screamed.

The belt hit my legs again and again, and I began to cry. My legs were on fire. I heard a car door open and shut. He drove away.

CHAPTER FOUR

On Saturday the shop was always busy. I put on my best dress and went to help. Everybody was talking about a group of German spies.

'The police got them . . . on the coast . . . small rubber boat . . . dirty Nazis!' I listened and put the whole story together, then I went to tell my parents the news.

My mother was selling shoes.

'Hi, mother,' I said. 'The police have caught some German spies!'

She looked at me. 'Have you eaten lunch? Where are Sharon and Ruth?'

'Ruth is cleaning the house and Sharon went to her friend's house. Is the shop busy today?'

'No, and I don't want *you* here. Why don't you go to Edna Louise's house?'

She made me angry. 'Edna Louise and everybody have gone on holiday. You know that. I want to work here.'

Mother stopped work and looked at me again. I saw that she was thinking something important. 'Maybe Miss Reeves can cut your hair today,' she said and picked up the telephone.

'Mother, listen to me!' I said, my voice high and loud. 'I don't want Miss Reeves to cut my hair. I like my hair. It's the best thing I have.'

'Aren't you **ashamed** to look so untidy?'

She was ashamed, not me. She was a beautiful woman and she had an ugly daughter. She telephoned Miss Reeves.

'I don't want to go,' I said.

'You're going,' my father said, behind me.

'Don't hit her,' my mother said quickly.

'You have two minutes to get to Miss Reeves' place or I'm going to hit you hard. Understand?'

I nodded.

'Answer me,' he said.

'Yes, **sir**.'

I went to Miss Reeves. When she finished with my hair, I cried and cried because I was now more ugly than before.

♦

I cleaned the hideout and sat looking out of the window thinking about my hair. Suddenly I saw somebody outside – a man with dark hair and a blue shirt running near the railway. I could see the word 'prisoner' on his back. A train was coming towards him. Then I knew who it was – it was Anton. He was escaping from the prison! I ran down the stairs and called his name but he did not hear me because of the noise of the train. I ran faster, waved my arms and shouted, 'Anton! Anton, it's me – Patty!'

He turned his head and saw me. He looked frightened, then pleased. He held out his hand and touched my fingers. I held his hand until the train disappeared.

♦

At 9.30 that night all the lights in the house went off. I went quietly into the kitchen. Anton was very hungry. I took some chicken and potatoes from the refrigerator and put them in a bag.

Suddenly I saw somebody outside – a man with dark hair and a blue shirt running near the railway.

'Who's in the kitchen?' my father shouted from his bedroom.

'It's nobody, just me.'

'Get some food and go to bed.'

I took the chicken and potatoes out of the bag, put them back in the refrigerator and went back to my room.

♦

The next morning I stayed in bed until my father went to work. When I went into the kitchen, the newspaper was on the table. On the front page was the story of the Nazi spies. It said there were many more spies in America: 'Any person who is a spy will die.'

I felt cold, afraid. Was I a spy if I helped Anton?

I took some more food from the refrigerator and went to the hideout above the garage. I climbed up.

'Anton – it's me! Anton!'

Suddenly the door opened and a hand pulled me in. 'Come in! Don't shout my name!' he said. 'You must be careful!'

'I'm sorry. I thought you weren't here.'

'Well, I am.' He smiled at me.

'I brought you some food,' I said.

I opened the bag. He was looking at me. I turned my head. I was not very pretty to look at after Miss Reeves' haircut.

Anton ate the food hungrily and told me about his family. His father, a teacher, hated Hitler.

'So why don't people in Germany fight Hitler?' I asked.

'They don't want to die,' Anton replied.

I asked him about his mother.

'My mother is wonderful in every way,' he said. 'She's kind and friendly. She sings beautifully, she knows the names of flowers, she likes to laugh. I have one sister called Hannah.'

'Why have you escaped from the prison?' I asked. 'The war will end soon. Then you can go home.'

'How long until the war ends? I hated that prison. I had to get out, I had to be free.'

'I'm glad you're here,' I said. 'I want you to be safe. How did you escape?'

He laughed. 'You remember the ring you sold me – the one with stones like diamonds? I told one of the guards they *were* diamonds. I gave it to him and he helped me to escape.' Then he asked, 'But why are you helping me, Patty? Is your family German? Bergen is a German name.'

'My family is from Luxembourg, not Germany. And Bergen is a Jewish name.'

His mouth opened. 'Jewish?' He pointed at me. 'You're Jewish?'

I thought he knew. I thought everybody knew we were Jewish. I nodded. Suddenly he began to laugh. 'This is funny,' he said. 'A Jewish girl helping a German soldier. Tell me, Patty, why *are* you helping me?'

Didn't he know? 'I just don't want anything bad to happen to you,' I said.

Anton turned his face away from me and nodded. I think he understood.

CHAPTER FIVE

There were a lot of people on Main Street talking, excited. They were talking about Anton's escape.

'You think he wanted to meet those other spies?' one man asked.

'I don't know,' his friend replied. 'He disappeared from the prison. I think somebody helped him to escape. I think there are Nazis everywhere.'

Two policemen from the city came into the shop to talk to my father. They showed him a photograph of Anton.

'Do you know this man?'

'He came into my shop with some of the other prisoners,' my father said. 'He spoke good English. But I don't like talking to Germans.'

'Do you remember anything special about this man?'

Sister Parker told the policemen that I spoke to the prisoner that day and they began to question me. 'You spoke to him? What did he say?'

I hid my face in my hands and started to cry. My father came over. 'What is it? What's happened?'

'We just want some information,' the policeman said. 'Mr Bergen, we must find this prisoner. He's dangerous. It's possible your daughter can remember something to help us.' He turned to me. 'We're fighting the Germans because they're bad people. They hurt children. Do you understand that?'

'Perfectly,' I said.

'Good. Then tell me what the German said.'

I told him Anton bought a pencil sharpener – a red one. Nothing important.

'Do you remember anything special about this man?'

'Yes, I do,' I said. 'He was very polite.'

◆

We heard about Anton's escape on the radio news. 'The police are searching for a German prisoner of war, Frederick Anton Reiker, who escaped yesterday from a prison near Jenkinsville, Arkansas. He's twenty-two years old, has dark hair and speaks good English. He's very dangerous.'

A young woman came into the shop. She said she was a reporter and wanted to speak to Sheriff Cauldwell. I offered to take her to his office.

We went in her car to the Sheriff's office. When she came out, she said, 'Do you know how to get to the prison, too?'

I showed her the way. 'Is it interesting being a reporter?' I asked.

She smiled at me. I could see she liked my question. 'What's your name?'

'Patty Bergen.'

'I'm Charlene Madlee. A reporter has to love words and to be interested in everything. Are you, Patty?'

'Yes, I am. It makes my father angry sometimes – he says I ask too many questions. And I like words. I use them all the time and I read dictionaries.'

'Really?'

'Yes. I try to find a word I don't understand and then I write it down.'

Charlene stopped the car outside the prison. A guard with a gun asked what she wanted.

'I'm a reporter. I want to see Major Wroper, the prison boss.'

We went to Major Wroper's office. Before we went in, Charlene gave me some paper and a pencil. 'OK, Patty. You want to be a reporter so you can help me. Write down everything you think is important about the prisoner who escaped.'

Major Wroper stood up when we walked into the room.

'Can I help you, Miss Madlee?' he asked.

'What I want to know, sir, is this: how was it possible for a prisoner to escape from here?'

'This is a very safe prison,' Major Wroper replied. 'We have guards, dogs, we're always very careful. We just don't understand how he got out. The police are trying to find out what happened.'

He told us that Anton ate his evening meal and went to his room. Later he just disappeared. The guards and dogs could not find him.

'Do you think he wanted to meet those other Nazi spies?' Charlene asked.

'No, I don't think so.'

'Can I talk to some of the people who knew Reiker?'

'Oh yes, of course,' Major Wroper said, and called another guard. We spoke to a doctor who knew Anton.

'Do you think he went to meet the spies?' Charlene asked.

'No, I don't think so. I think he just wanted to be free. Some of our prisoners are real Nazis but Reiker wasn't like that. He was interested in books and ideas. He seemed to be a good man.'

Charlene drove us back to town. I thought about the doctor's

'Do you think he wanted to meet those other Nazi spies?' Charlene asked.

words and I stopped being frightened. Suddenly I felt very, very happy.

CHAPTER SIX

I took some more food to Anton in the hideout. 'I've brought you some food and clean clothes,' I said. Anton touched my hand and smiled at me.

In the bag was one of my father's shirts, an expensive blue one.

I gave the shirt to Anton. Would he like it? Maybe it wasn't a nice shirt. He looked at it and I saw how pleased he was.

'Thanks,' he said, touching my face.

I told him about the police who were looking for him.

'I don't understand,' he said. 'I'm only a soldier. Why are they looking for me?'

'Because the police caught some German spies and they think you're trying to meet them. But you're OK here – you're safe. I can bring you food and books and anything you need. Tell me what you want!'

He looked at me. 'I want to be brave like you, P.B.'

He called me P.B. and he made the letters sound beautiful.

'After the war, I shall tell my family about you. How an American Jewish girl helped me.'

I wanted to ask him to take me with him, back to Germany. Then his hand touched my hair, my short, ugly hair.

'Why are you suddenly so quiet?' Anton asked.

I was angry. Angry with Miss Reeves who made me ugly and angry with Anton who made me want to be pretty. Angry with myself for thinking that a man like him could love a girl like me. I stood up to go.

'I don't want to talk about it.' I reached the door. He held his hand out to me but I closed the door between us.

◆

I sat down near the house. He's only being nice to me because I help him, I thought. He's nice to me because he likes me. He's handsome, I'm ugly. But being pretty is not important. He's laughing at me. Why did I meet him? How am I going to live without him? The thoughts went round and round in my head. Somebody called my name. It was Freddy Dowd. He sat down next to me. A minute later I heard my father's car stop in front of our house.

'Oh Harry, leave her,' my mother said, from inside the car.

Me? What did I do? Oh God – it's Freddy! 'Go away, Freddy!' I said. 'Please go home!'

My father's face was white and angry. 'I told you not to talk to Freddy,' he shouted.

It was Freddy Dowd. He sat down next to me.

'I can explain –'

My mother stood between us. 'Harry, Harry, leave her. Please!'

With one hand he pushed her and she fell onto the grass.

'I'll make you listen to me!' he shouted.

I moved away from him. 'I can explain! I was sitting there and Freddy came along a minute ago and sat down. That's all.'

He moved towards me. I tried to keep away from him but he caught my arm.

I screamed when he began to hit me, then I fell to the ground. Oh God, can't you help me?

Everything was quiet. I lay there with my eyes closed. Has he finished hitting me? I thought. But he stood over me and I heard the sound of his belt. He lifted his arm to hit me with the belt and I saw Anton behind my father, running towards us, ready to fight.

'No,' I shouted. 'Go away! Go away!'

Anton stopped. His face was different, angry. Really angry. Then he put his hands over his eyes and ran back to the garage.

CHAPTER SEVEN

I was in the kitchen with Ruth. 'Now I want you to tell me: who's the man?' she asked. 'The man who ran from the garage? The man who wanted to save you from your father. You hear me, girl?'

'The man – the man –' I did not know what to say. She looked at me carefully.

'The man is my friend,' I said.

'You've hidden him in the room above the garage?'

'Yes.'

'Is he the man the police are searching for? The one from the prison?'

'Yes.' Immediately I felt better because Ruth knew. She shook her head sadly.

'It's OK,' I said. 'You sometimes help me because you're my friend. Well, Anton's my friend and I have to help him.'

I took some food. 'That's no breakfast for a man,' Ruth said. 'I'll make you some hot cakes and coffee.'

I threw my arms round her. 'Oh Ruth, you're good, good, good! His name is Anton – Mr Frederick Anton Reiker. You and Anton are the only friends I have.'

Ruth nodded slowly. 'I know, girl.'

'He talks to me and tells me things because he's my friend, Ruth. He likes me. He really likes me.'

'I know that too.' If Ruth knew something then it *was* true. 'He came running from the garage because he was unhappy. He saw how your father was hurting you. When someone loves you, they put themselves in danger.'

◆

I went across to the garage. Anton opened the door immediately when I arrived at the hideout. 'How are you?' he asked. His face was worried.

'I'm OK.'

'Are you sure?' He looked at my legs where my father hit me.

'Oh, yes, thanks.'

'About yesterday –' he began.

'It's OK, Anton. I'm OK, really.'

'No,' he said angrily. 'It's not OK! Listen to me, P.B. Why did your father hit you?'

How can I explain something I don't understand myself, I thought. Sometimes I think my father hits me because something is wrong with me. Sometimes I think it is because something is wrong with *him*.

'I don't like your father,' Anton said.

'That's OK,' I said, pleased that Anton was taking my side. 'Sometimes I don't like him much.'

'Do you know what your father did after he hit you?'

'He probably went into the house, smoked a cigarette, washed his hands and ate a large dinner,' I said.

'No. He watched Ruth help you into the house. He was talking to himself. Then he came into the garage. I heard him say, "Nobody loves me."'

'Anton, that doesn't sound like my father. I don't understand. How can he hurt me then worry that nobody loves him?'

'I met your father once,' Anton said. 'When we came into the shop to buy hats. He didn't want to speak to me because I am a German.'

'I remember.'

'People who do not want to talk to others can be very dangerous. If Hitler, for example, could talk to other people he would not be so dangerous.'

'Do you think my father is like Hitler?'

'I don't know. Maybe they both need to hurt people.'

Suddenly I laughed. 'I'm glad you're teaching me to think

about things, Anton. I want you to teach me everything you know. I want to be clever, more than I want to be pretty.'

'You are already clever and pretty, P.B.' he said seriously.

'Me?'

'Yes.'

'Then why don't other people think so?'

'They will. You're different to other girls.'

A voice called from downstairs. Anton looked frightened.

'It's OK,' I said. 'It's Ruth. She's made some hot cakes and coffee for us.'

'Why did you tell her about me?'

'She saw you run out of the garage! She saw that you wanted to help me.'

Anton smiled. 'I did want to help you. I always try to stay out of danger then I do something dangerous for you. But I'm glad I did.'

CHAPTER EIGHT

That morning, Anton came over to the house for breakfast. Ruth, Anton and I sat at the table in the kitchen. Ruth liked Anton and Anton liked Ruth. They talked about food and about the war.

'The world's a bad place,' Ruth said. 'Do you think it's going to get better?'

'I don't know,' Anton replied. 'All I know is that love is better than hate.'

Suddenly we heard a car outside the house. 'Mr Bergen!' Ruth said. 'It's him! Hide Anton under your bed, Patty. Quick!'

It was not my father, it was a neighbour. Her car moved away.

We sat at the table. 'I'm sorry,' Anton said. 'When I'm here, you're both in danger. I'll leave tonight.'

'I'll give you some food and money,' Ruth said quickly.

'You are already clever and pretty, P.B.' he said seriously.

I did not want him to leave. 'We're not frightened. It's not safe for you to leave, Anton. Tell him, Ruth!'

But Ruth did not say anything.

♦

When we sat down to eat dinner that evening, I kissed my father and my mother.

'I like your tie,' I said. 'Is it from the shop?' He said that it was.

'Is the shop busy? Lots of customers?'

'Eat your dinner and don't ask so many questions.'

'There's a doctor in Boston who says it's good to talk at dinner.'

'And I told you to be quiet and eat!' He was angry again.

I decided what to do. My father and my mother will be happy when I leave, I thought.

♦

I walked down the street with Ruth when she went home. At the corner she told me to go home.

'Before I go, I want to say goodbye.'

She smiled. 'Don't go near the garage. Anton's going to leave tonight and you can't help if the police catch him.'

'Don't worry,' I said. I took her hand. 'Goodbye Ruth.'

At home, I looked round my bedroom for the last time then I put some clothes and shoes into a bag. I looked at Sharon. She was sleeping.

'Be good,' I said. She opened her eyes sleepily, took my hand and closed her eyes again.

♦

I left my bag at the bottom of the garage stairs and climbed into the hideout.

'Anton!' I said quietly. 'It's me! Patty!'

The door opened. 'Quiet,' he said and pulled me into the room.

'I thought – I thought you weren't here,' I said and began to cry.

Anton held my hand. 'You know I can't stay. You've always known that, P.B.'

'No I haven't!' I said. 'Anton, I won't be any trouble. What I'm trying to say is – don't leave me. Please take me with you.'

'I can't. It's impossible. You know that. But if you are saying that you love me –'

'Yes,' I answered. 'Yes.'

'I love you too, Patty. And I'll miss you.'

He opened the door and climbed down then held out his hand to me. The moon was bright and I could see his face, a face I could never forget.

He looked at his watch. 'The train comes at ten-fifteen. I'll help you get back into the house. There's still time.'

'No, thanks. I can get back OK. Here's some money – only four dollars. It's all Ruth and I had.'

He took the money. 'Thanks for this, for everything. I have something for you. It belonged to my father and to his father.' Anton looked down at his finger. 'This ring was my grandfather's when he was a teacher at the university. The ring is yours, P.B.' He spoke quietly. 'Am I still your teacher? Then I want you to learn one final lesson: I want you to remember you are a **valuable** person and that you have a friend who loves you.'

'I will, Anton. I'll remember.'

I lifted my hand. Our lips touched for a second. When I opened my eyes, Anton was gone. I stood there not wanting to move, touching the gold ring on my finger.

Then, far away, I heard the train coming.

CHAPTER NINE

I thought about Anton all the time. I kept his ring round my neck and every time I touched it, I thought about him. I wanted to talk about it, to tell somebody about Anton's special present to me.

'The ring is yours, P.B.'

'Have you seen my ring?' I asked Sister Parker.

'Did your boyfriend give it to you?' she said.

'Boyfriend? No,' I replied, frightened.

'Who gave it to you?'

What could I tell her? I lied, of course. 'It happened on Monday. I was walking home from school and I saw an old man. He looked old because his hair was white. He asked me if I had any food because he was hungry. I took him home and I gave him a good meal. When he finished eating he said thank you. He said he wanted to give me something and he put this ring on my finger.'

Sister Parker nodded and I felt proud of my story.

'Then he said he wasn't really poor. He told people he was poor so he could find the good people in the world. He said that because I'm good I'm going to get a present on my eighteenth birthday. A valuable present.'

'Hey, Mr Bergen,' Sister Parker called. 'Is this ring gold?'

'What are you talking about?' My father walked across the shop. 'Whose ring is this?'

Sister Parker looked at me. 'It's Patty's.'

I was stupid. Why did I tell that story to Sister Parker? My father looked at the ring.

'It's real gold,' he said. 'How did you get this?'

'Well, last Monday – you remember last Monday –'

'Be quick!' he said.

'I'm trying to tell you. I met this man and I gave him some food –'

'What happened?' My father was very angry. 'Who was he?'

'A man. A hungry man. I told you.'

'What did he do to you?'

'He said thank you. He was very polite.'

'You're lying, you dirty girl.'

'No sir, that's true!'

'**Liar**! Tell me the **truth**! He touched you. He put his hands on you, you dirty, dirty girl!'

My father was very angry. 'Who was he?'

He lifted his hand and I closed my eyes. He hit me and I fell on the floor.

Sister Parker helped me to stand up. 'You're going to be OK,' she said. 'I'll bring you a cold towel for your face.'

I heard my father speaking on the telephone. 'Is Sheriff Cauldwell in his office? Ask him to come to the shop now, please.'

My mother was shouting. 'Why did you call the Sheriff? Harry, what's happened?'

My face was hot and it hurt. I felt sick. 'Anton,' I said to myself. 'Why did you leave me?' I wanted to die.

Outside, a car stopped. I heard Sheriff Cauldwell's voice.

'Get up,' my father said. 'Sheriff Cauldwell wants to talk to you. There are a lot of things he wants to know. You understand?'

I stood up and looked at him.

'Answer me!' he shouted. I began to cry again.

Sheriff Cauldwell spoke softly. 'Patty, tell me what happened. Did this old man hurt you? Don't be frightened. Tell me what happened.'

'Can I have my ring?' I asked.

'Harry, give the girl her ring,' he said to my father. 'Now tell me who gave it to you.'

I told the story to Sheriff Cauldwell.

'Did anything happen? Did he hurt you?'

'Oh no, sir.'

'Did he touch you anywhere on your body?'

'Oh no, sir. But –'

'But what?' he asked quickly.

'He touched my hand to say goodbye.'

Sheriff Cauldwell laughed. 'Well, Harry,' he said to my father. 'It sounds OK to me.'

'I'm still not happy,' my father said. 'I don't **believe** her. Why did he give her this valuable ring? I think she's lying.'

'Why did he give you the ring?' Sheriff Cauldwell asked.

'Well sir,' I tried to think of something to say, then it came to me. I looked at my father. 'The old man gave me the ring because he was proud of me. He said he always wanted to have a daughter like me.'

CHAPTER TEN

It was the end of the summer – the summer of my Anton. I sat in the hideout. When I'm eighteen, I thought, I'm going to Germany to find Anton. I'm going to be beautiful when I'm eighteen, I'm going to be beautiful for Anton.

'Patty! Hi, Patty!' Ruth called. 'Your father wants you.'

'I haven't done anything,' I said. 'Is he angry?'

'No, I don't think he's angry. Just be polite to him.'

'Do you think he'll take my ring away?' I asked. 'He can't

have it. I won't give it to him!' I pulled the ring off my finger and put it in Ruth's pocket.

My father was in the house with two men – the two policemen who questioned me about Anton in the shop.

'I'm Mr Pierce,' one of the policemen said. 'I want to ask you some questions.' He asked me about the old man I said I gave food to. How old was he? Where did he come from? Then he showed me a photograph. 'Is this the man?'

The photograph – it was him. Anton. 'Sir?'

'Was this the man you gave food to?'

I did not know what to say. I did not want to hurt Anton. 'It doesn't look like him,' I said, slowly.

Mr Pierce pulled something from a bag. 'Have you seen this shirt before?' It was my father's shirt, the shirt I gave to Anton.

'Well?'

'I think I've seen it before. But all shirts look the same.'

'Your father says this is his shirt,' Pierce said. 'Did you give it to this man? The prisoner?'

The shirt was dirty. 'Blood,' I said. 'Is this blood?'

Pierce did not answer.

'Blood!' I screamed. 'Have you hurt him?'

'Hurt who?'

'You know! The man who was wearing this shirt. Frederick Anton Reiker. Is he OK?'

Pierce gave me a piece of paper. It said: 'POLICE SHOT FREDERICK ANTON REIKER EARLY THIS MORNING. HE DIED IN A NEW YORK HOSPITAL AT 10.15 A.M.'

I did not believe him. It was not true. Suddenly I began to scream. 'You killed him!'

♦

I lay down on the bed. I heard Pierce talking on the telephone. 'The girl says she helped Reiker. She knew he was a prisoner.

'Blood,' I said. 'Is this blood?'

We're taking her to Memphis to ask her some more questions. She's going to stay with her grandparents.'

My father came into the room. He looked sad. 'I don't understand,' he said. 'You're a Jewish girl and you helped a Nazi. Why?' He started to shout. 'Tell me why!'

'Because he was good to me.'

'I don't believe you. Did he touch you? Did he? You dirty girl!'

'No! Anton was a good man – a much better man than you!'

'I'm not a Nazi,' my father shouted. 'I'm ashamed of you! I hate you! I've always hated you!'

Ruth came in. 'Don't say that, Mr Bergen. Patty's just a child. She helped a man, that's all.'

'Go away, Ruth,' my father said.

'No sir. Patty isn't a bad girl –'

My father pulled five dollars out of his pocket. 'Take this and leave now, Ruth. I don't want you in my house,' he said. Ruth turned and left the room, without a word.

♦

I walked down the street with the policemen. We were going to Memphis. There were a lot of people near the shop.

'Nazi! Nazi!' a woman shouted.

'Jew Nazi! Jew Nazi!' a man screamed.

Later, somebody broke all the windows of my father's shop.

♦

My grandparents were kind to me.

'Are you angry with me?' I asked them.

'Of course we're not angry,' my grandmother said. 'You gave food to a hungry man, that's all. Is that bad? The police want to talk to you today. And a reporter telephoned – Miss Charlene Madlee. She's coming to see you tonight.'

'I don't think they're going to send Patty to prison,' Charlene said to my grandfather when she came that evening. 'She's only twelve years old. Many people will hear this story about a Jewish girl and a German prisoner. It shows that people can be friends, people from different countries. I don't think Patty is going to prison – but I think they'll probably send her to a special school for a time.'

CHAPTER ELEVEN

I tried to explain to the police that I helped Anton because he was a good man who wanted to be free, but nobody listened. They asked me if Anton frightened me and made me help him. They asked me if I was too young to understand that Anton was an escaped prisoner. I told the truth; I was not stupid. I knew

Anton was an escaped prisoner and I helped him because I wanted to. They sent me to the Arkansas Special School for Girls for six months.

It was dark when we arrived at the school. It looked no different to any other school – but no, there was something different. The doors and windows were all locked. Now *I* was a prisoner.

◆

I woke up at six-thirty one morning. It was my thirty-second morning in the school. I lay in bed and thought about what happened to me. Thought about living with my grandparents in Memphis. Thought about going far away where nobody knew me. Then I escaped into my special **dream**.

When I'm eighteen, I thought, I'll have some money and I'll take a train to New York and a ship to Germany. In Germany I'll telephone Anton's mother.

'Mrs Reiker,' I'll say. 'I'm an American. My name is Patricia Ann Bergen. I knew your son, Anton. We were friends when he was a prisoner in America.'

'You knew Anton? You helped him? Where are you?' she'll ask.

Then I'll tell her I am in Germany. 'Come and see me,' she'll say. 'Come and stay with us.'

'Hey, Nazi, wake up,' Mavis McCall said – she was the other girl in my room.

'Don't call me Nazi.'

'What do you want me to call you? Nazi or Spy?' Mavis was the only girl in school who spoke to me.

Later that day, I had a visitor. I saw her in the visitors' room, looking out through the locked window.

'Ruth?' I said.

She turned and put her arms round me. 'Patty. How are you? Are you OK?' I put my head on her shoulder. For the first time in weeks I felt safe.

'Hey, Nazi, wake up,' Mavis McCall said.

'You're very thin,' she said.

'The food isn't very good. Tell me what's happening in Jenkinsville.'

'Well, I have a new job now, working for the schoolteacher. I came here on the bus.'

'That's a long journey,' I said, trying to smile. I had not smiled for a long time.

'Has your mother visited you?' Ruth asked.

'She's been ill. She says the journey is too long. Have you seen her or my father?'

'I saw your mother in the shop with Sharon.'

'Did she say anything? Did she ask about me?'

'Of course she did!' Ruth looked away from me.

'Tell me the truth. What did she say?'

'Not much. She said she sometimes gets letters from you and she sent you a coat. She said – she said I was the only person who knew how to **control** you.'

That made me angry. 'That's all they think about – controlling me. Why can't I just be myself? What's wrong with me, Ruth? Why am I always in trouble?'

Ruth shook her head. 'There's nothing wrong with you, Patty.'

'There is!' I shouted. 'I'm always in trouble. People hate me!'

'That isn't true. I love you,' Ruth said, 'and I'm not the only one. Anton loved you, too. I saw that when he ran out from the garage when your father was hitting you. I saw that he loved you.'

'Is that true? He gave me his ring so that I wouldn't forget him but I lost the ring and now I can't remember if he loved me or not.'

Ruth opened her bag. 'You didn't lose your ring, girl. You gave it to me to look after when your father came home with those two policemen that day. Remember?'

I touched the ring with my lips. 'He did love me,' I said to Ruth. 'Maybe one day my mother and father will love me too.'

'You just remember you're a good person,' Ruth said.

I knew that Ruth understood. I always thought my parents hated me because I was a bad person but I was not bad. It was not important what other people thought or said about me. I was not a bad person and Ruth knew that.

'I don't ever want to go home again,' I said.

'You have to. You're too young to run away. When you leave this place, you go home and finish school. Then you can be something – a nurse or a teacher. Something important.'

'I know what I want to be,' I said. 'A reporter. Charlene Madlee wrote to me. She says that if I write something it'll go in the newspaper.'

I heard someone coming and the noise of keys. Miss Laud, the head teacher, stood at the door.

'That's the end of visiting time. You must leave immediately,' she said to Ruth.

'Miss Laud, please! She came so far. She's the only visitor I've had. Please can she stay a few more minutes?'

Miss Laud's eyes were cold. 'You always want too much! You tell everyone you don't like it here. You only like black people and Nazis!'

'Miss Laud,' Ruth said loudly. 'You leave this child. I'm going now.'

I threw my arms round Ruth's neck. 'Please take me with you, Ruth. Please don't leave me here.'

She dried my face. 'You know I can't do that, girl. Everything is going to be all right. Just wait and see. One day you'll wake up and be happy again.'

She moved towards the door. She looked old and tired. Suddenly I wanted to give her something, something valuable, but I had nothing.

'I don't have anything to give you,' I said. 'I have nothing at all to give you.'

'You've got love to give, Patty. There's nothing better than that.'

◆

I threw my arms round Ruth's neck. 'Please take me with you, Ruth. Please don't leave me here.'

I watched her leave. I was **drowning** and she was the only person who could save me. But that wasn't true. Ruth could only help me some of the way. I must learn to swim for myself.

There was so much I wanted to say to her but I could not find the right words. I almost called goodbye, but I didn't. The door closed and Ruth was gone.

For a few minutes I stood there, not moving. Was it possible for a new swimmer like me to save herself? I had a lot of time in front of me to find out.

EXERCISES

Vocabulary Work

Look back at the 'Dictionary Words' in this book. Check that you understand them.

1 Two of the words describe things you can wear. Which are they?

2 Six of the words are verbs or parts of verbs. Which are they?

3 Match these words and phrases:

hideout	expensive
sharpener	something which really happened
valuable	someone who does not tell the truth
sir	a secret place
dream	name given to an important man
truth	used to make points on pencils
liar	something you hope will happen

Comprehension

Chapters 1–2

1 Why are the people at the station angry when the German prisoners arrive?

2 Who is Ruth?

Chapters 3–4

3 Why is the summer 'endless'? Why is Patty bored?

4 What does Anton use the diamond ring for?

5 Why is Anton surprised to find that Patty is Jewish?

Chapters 5–6

6 What is Charlene Madlee's job? Why is she in Jenkinsville?

7 Why does Patty's father hit her?

Chapters 7–8

8 Anton decides to leave the hideout. Why?

9 Why does Anton give Patty his grandfather's ring?

Chapters 9–10

10 Why does Patty show the ring to Sister Parker?

11 What happens to Anton?

12 Why does Mr Bergen tell Ruth to leave the house?

Chapter 11

13 Where do the police send Patty?

14 Ruth gives something important to Patty. What is it – and *why* is it important?

Discussion

1 What sort of man is Patty's father? Why do you think he is always so angry with her?

2 Why is everyone surprised when Patty, a Jewish girl, helps Anton, a German soldier? Do you think she is right to help him? Why or why not?

Writing

You are Ruth and you are writing a letter to your son Robert describing the events of the summer and what happened to Patty and Anton. Write about 150 words.

or

You are Charlene Madlee. Write about 150 words for a newspaper describing how Anton escaped from prison and how Patty helped him.